Contents

Madam Spry
and the
Blue Diamond

♡ *Joy Cowley*

Joy Cowley

Signatures
Madam Spry and the Blue Diamond

This edition published by
Clean Slate Press Ltd.
9 George St, Mt Eden
Auckland 1024, New Zealand
www.cleanslatepress.com

Author: Joy Cowley
Designed by: McGraw-Hill Australia Pty Ltd.
Illustrations by: Gaston Vanzet

Text © Joy Cowley
Design and illustrations © McGraw-Hill Australia Pty Ltd. 2007
This edition published by Clean Slate Press Ltd. with the permission
of McGraw-Hill Australia Pty Ltd.
Originally published by McGraw-Hill Australia Pty Ltd. 2007

© This edition 2008 Clean Slate Press Ltd.

22 21 20 19 18 17 16
11 10 9 8 7 6 5 4 3

ISBN: 978-1-877454-36-3

Printed in China

① Help needed

Madam Spry was a very sly spy who liked to sing. When she sang, car batteries went flat and birds dropped from trees. But that did not stop her. In the shower, she raised her voice in song although she knew it wrecked the plumbing in her apartment.

Madam Spry is a very sly spy.
A very sly spy is she.
She puts her spyglass to her eye
to see what she can see.

What she saw, in fact, was her dog, Hugo, scratching at the shower door with a yellow letter in his mouth. It was an urgent message from Inspector Crabbe of the city police.

Dear Violet Spry,
We need your help. The famous blue
diamond has been stolen from the movie
star Sonya Sweet. Come with all speed.
Yours sincerely,
Alex Crabbe

All speed meant top gear for Madam Spry. In five seconds, she dressed in her red leather spy suit with its thirteen pockets and her fly-foot boots. She checked that she had her spyglass and her phone watch. Because the lift in her building was slow, she opened her window and ran down the outside wall, her boots sucking onto the concrete with the speed of a runaway fly. On the way down, she waved to people having breakfast in their apartments.

"Good morning."

"Hi there, folks!"

"Have a nice day!"

It gave her exquisite pleasure to see someone swallow an egg whole or spill a cup of coffee in their lap.

On the ground, she leaped on the back of a passing bus and pressed her phone watch.

"Inspector Crabbe? I'll meet you at Sonya Sweet's mansion in six minutes."

The bus driver, who knew Madam Spry well, stopped at the next traffic light.

"You!" he yelled. "Pay for a ticket or get off my bus!"

"But I'm not in your bus!" she yelled back.

"On or in makes no difference," he said. "No ticket—no ride."

Madam Spry dropped to the ground and said a word too rude for this story.

The driver sniffed. "Some people are very dishonest," he said as the bus pulled away.

"And some people are downright picky!" she bellowed after him.

The argument had upset Madam Spry, but there was another way of getting to Sonya Sweet on time. From a pocket she took a coil of spider wire, made a loop in one end and flicked the loop over the clock tower. She swung back and forth like a red pendulum, faster, faster, and then she let go. Straight and true, she flew into the next street, where she landed on top of the city museum. From there it was only a short jump onto the roof of Sonya Sweet's white marble mansion.

Inspector Crabbe was waiting. "What are you doing up there, Violet?" he called.

Quickly she took out her spyglass. "Checking for clues, Alex."

"Oh, I don't think the thief got away through the roof," he said. "There aren't any doors to the roof."

"I know that," she said, as she ran down the wall in her fly-foot boots. "But one can never be too careful when there's been a robbery."

"That's right," he said thoughtfully, tugging the ends of his moustache. "Violet, you are a super spy. You leave no stone unturned."

"Of course, Alex." She tucked her spyglass in a pocket. "Now let's talk to poor Sonya Sweet."

② *Tears and suspects*

Sonya Sweet had curly yellow hair and eyes like startled blue daisies. She dabbed at her eyes with a silken lace handkerchief as she led Madam Spry and Inspector Crabbe through the hall. "I don't know what I'll do!' she said, "My boyfriend, Floyd, paid the earth for that diamond. He was going to put it in my engagement ring."

"Isn't the diamond insured?" asked Madam Spry.

"Yes, but that's not the point!" Sonya wept. "There is only one blue diamond. It's been stolen and I'll never get another like it."

"There, there," said Inspector Crabbe, patting her on the shoulder. "We'll get it back, my dear."

The lounge room was as big as a ballroom, and all white except for a huge tank of tropical fish along one wall. Madam Spry and Inspector Crabbe stopped to admire the yellow and black zebra fish, and the parrotfish bright green among pink coral.

"Do you like fish?" Sonya asked.

"In batter," said the inspector, "with chips."

At the far end of the room, sat Floyd, Sonya's boyfriend. He too looked extremely sad. "Of course, the diamond was in the safe. The thief must have known how to open it." He sighed from the depths of his heart. "A magnificent blue diamond as big as a walnut! The only gift worthy of my princess!"

Sonya burst into noisy tears and threw herself into Floyd's arms. Bravely, but sadly, he comforted her.

Inspector Crabbe coughed. "Excuse me. Too much PDA."

Floyd unglued his lips. "PDA?"

"Public display of affection," explained Crabbe. "If you don't mind, we'd like to examine the crime scene. Shall we start with the safe?"

Sonya dried her big blue eyes. "If I were you, Inspector, I'd start with Miss Jasmine Raintree."

"Not Jasmine Raintree, the actress," said Madam Spry.

"Yes, indeed," said Floyd. "Jasmine is madly jealous of Sonya because Sonya was the leading role in a big new film. Jasmine has been saying nasty things about Sonya to the newspapers."

Sonya nodded. "Miss Raintree was here yesterday. The gardener saw her walk into the house." She started to weep again. "To think I once considered her my friend!"

"Where were you yesterday?" Madam Spry asked.

Floyd took Sonya's hand. "We were in town, arranging our engagement party."

"Which will have to be cancelled," cried Sonya, turning to Floyd in a storm of weeping.

"PDA! PDA!" grunted Inspector Crabbe.

Madam Spry tossed a packet of tissues at Sonya Sweet. "When we've finished here, we'll interview Jasmine Raintree. Don't worry, Miss Sweet. We'll recover the blue diamond."

"I wouldn't count on it," Floyd said mournfully. "Jasmine has probably sold it already, in Europe or the Middle East."

At that, Sonya screamed and collapsed into Floyd's arms, and Inspector Crabbe hurried out of the room.

③ Jasmine's story

Inspector Crabbe was puzzled. "I haven't a clue," he said.

Madam Spry was also clueless but she would not say so. There were fingerprints on the front door and the hall that could belong to Jasmine Raintree. But there were no fingerprints on the safe.

"Gloves," suggested Inspector Crabbe.

"Why didn't she put on gloves before she opened the door?" Madam Spry asked.

"Because she didn't want the gardener to see her putting on gloves."

"Maybe the gardener was in on it," said Madam Spry.

The inspector shook his head. "Don't think so. No mud on the white carpet."

They drove in the inspector's car to the film set where Jasmine Raintree was acting in a new jungle adventure. She was wearing an imitation leopard skin and had yellow orchids in her long dark hair. She welcomed them, and invited them into her small and rather shabby make-up trailer; but her smile vanished the moment they mentioned Sonya Sweet.

"Don't utter that name in my presence!" she snarled.

Madam Spry took a miniature camera from a pocket and click, click, photographed the inside of the trailer. "You know that Sonya—that a certain person has lost her famous blue diamond."

"Serves her right for being careless," declared Jasmine.

"The diamond was stolen," said Inspector Crabbe. "We'd like you to help us with our enquiries."

"I can't help you." The actress leaned towards her mirror to put on her bright red lipstick. "I haven't been near the place."

"You were there yesterday," said Madam Spry.

"That's a lie!" Jasmine cried.

"The gardener saw you," Inspector Crabbe pointed out. "You went in the house."

The lipstick went up Jasmine's nose. "Another lie!" she squawked. "Let me tell you about Sonya Sweet. She's as sweet as a bucketful of vinegar. She's so jealous of me! She stole my part in a big film!"

"Weren't you once friends?" asked Inspector Crabbe.

"Friends?" Jasmine screamed. "She couldn't spell friendship if it was tattooed across her face!"

While the star was still screaming, Madam Spry took a fingerprint decoder out of another of her pockets and looked at the hairbrush and the lipstick holder. "Same fingerprints," she said. "You went through the front door and into the hall."

Jasmine Raintree shut her mouth. She put down her lipstick and folded her arms. "All right," she said. "Yesterday morning, Sonya called me and invited me around for coffee. But when I got to her house, there was no one home. I went in the door and called her name. When there was no answer, I went out again. That's all."

"Did you lock the front door behind you?"

"It wasn't locked," she said. "I just left it the way I found it."

At that moment, there was loud voice outside the trailer door. "Jasmine? We're ready to shoot the next scene."

"Excuse me," said Miss Raintree. "This is where I wrestle a rubber crocodile in a swimming pool." She stood up. "I can't say it's been nice talking to you."

"Wait! Your lipstick!" cried Madam Spry. "You look as though your nose is bleeding!"

But Miss Jasmine Raintree was out the door.

4 A horrible trip home

Madam Spry was in a thoroughly bad mood. She had not been able to solve the case of the stolen blue diamond. On the way home, she discovered that her spider wire on the clock tower had gone. Someone was probably using it as a clothes line. It had been a horrible day, she thought. But it was not over yet. Tired, she decided to take the slow old lift up to her apartment. On the way, she sang a song to comfort herself.

I'm a super spy,
don't you know, don't you know.
I will always find you wherever you go,
wherever you go.
If you try to get away,

I've a way to make you stay.
I'll just call my faithful hound, Hugo, Hugo.

Unfortunately, at the last "Hugo" the lift shuddered and stopped, and the lights went out.

Hugo, who could hear Madam Spry's voice anywhere in the building, came running. He whined in sympathy, but there was not much he could do. Madam Spry had to force open the trapdoor in the top of the lift and climb through it. Squeezing past cables in the dark meant grease on her spy suit. Blast! She walked carefully in her fly-foot boots, up the wall of the shaft, until she got to her floor. Then, taking her maxi-knife from one of her pockets, she inserted it between the doors and switched it on.

The knife hummed as it grew wider and forced the lift doors apart. Wider still, it made a gap that showed the face of an anxious dog. Madam Spry groaned. Why hadn't she bought a super-speed maxi-knife? The knife and the gap grew very slowly, until at last she could step through. She was so exhausted that she almost fell over her faithful hound.

"Hugo," she sighed. "I'm a failure. People will laugh at me. I feel so depressed."

Hugo understood. Back in the apartment, he opened the fridge with one swipe of his paw. With a swipe of the other paw, he rolled out a can of lemonade.

"Thank you, Hugo." Madam Spry took the lemonade to her office and switched on her computer. Within seconds she had accessed the world diamond market. She scanned the screen, looking for mention of a large blue diamond the size of a walnut. There was nothing.

Frustrated, she threw back her head and sang,

This is a crime without a clue.
It's not just the diamond that is blue.

She didn't manage another note before the computer's battery went flat.

Madam Spry stamped her feet. "Hugo," she said. "I think I'll give up spying and drive a bus."

5 Sparkling water

The next morning, Madam Spry was walking Hugo in the park when her phone watch whistled like a kettle. She held it to her ear and heard Inspector Crabbe's voice. "Violet, I've been thinking about the blue diamond case. Miss Raintree said that Miss Sweet invited her over for coffee. Maybe we should check that with Miss Sweet."

"Fine," said Madam Spry. "But I've got Hugo with me ..."

"Bring him too," said the inspector. "He doesn't bite people and he always wipes his feet on the doormat."

Minutes later, Inspector Crabbe and Madam Spy rang the door chimes of the white mansion.

Floyd and Sonya opened the door together. Sonya's daisy-blue eyes were wide with hope. She clapped her hands. "You've found my blue diamond!"

"No, not yet," said Inspector Crabbe.

Her eyes filled with tears and her pink lips trembled.

The inspector said quickly, "Let's go into the lounge. We'd like to check a couple of statements."

Hugo trotted at Madam Spry's side—but he didn't like the tropical fish. He barked and growled at them.

"Tell your dog to be quiet," said Floyd. "He's upsetting our fish."

Madam Spry dragged Hugo across the room and made him sit beside her.

"My dear Miss Sweet," said the inspector. "Forgive me for asking this. Did you invite Miss Raintree to your house, the morning the diamond was stolen?"

She looked surprised. "No! Why would I do that?"

Crabbe tugged at his moustache. "You are quite sure?"

"Of course I'm sure."

Floyd stood up. "Inspector, my Sonya would have nothing to do with that nasty woman."

"That's right." Sonya put her arms around Floyd's neck.

The inspector coughed. "It seems we'll have to have another talk with Miss Raintree," he said. "Come, Madam Spry."

"Wait!" said Madam Spry. "I think there's something wrong with Hugo."

She was right. Hugo was still growling at the tropical fish. The hairs on his neck were standing up like electric wires. Madam Spry let go of his lead and at once he bounded over to the big fish tank. He jumped up against it and barked loudly.

"Stop him!" cried Sonya. "He might break the glass!"

There's something fishy going on here, thought Madam Spry.

Floyd was angry. "Please go at once. Sonya's fish are very sensitive and if they get frightened they could die. Don't you think my princess has suffered enough this week?"

But Madam Spry already had her spyglass out. As she switched it to the ultraviolet beam, she smiled at Sonya and Floyd. "I told you we'd find your diamond!"

"What are you talking about?" said Sonya.

Madam Spry pointed the beam of light at the fish tank. There, in the water, glowed a pale blue stone the size of a walnut.

"It wasn't visible in normal light," said Madam Spry. "The fish tank was the perfect hiding place."

"That fiendish Jasmine Raintree!" screamed Sonya Sweet. "She hid my diamond out of sheer spite!"

Floyd put his arms around her. "How could she do this to you, my darling?"

Inspector Crabbe shook his head. "Miss Raintree's fingerprints were not on the safe. I suspect something else happened. Two people hid their own diamond and said it was stolen. They invited Miss Raintree here to establish a suspect. They planned to spend the insurance money and then, much later, they would sell the diamond to a foreign buyer."

"That's utter nonsense!" cried Floyd.

Hugo sat down and wagged his tail.

"I'm arresting you both for fraud," said Inspector Crabbe.

Sonya Sweet screamed like a fire siren. She lay on the floor, yelling, beating her fists and drumming her heels on the carpet. Floyd tried to quieten her.

"Too much PDT," said Inspector Crabbe.

"Don't you mean PDA?" asked Floyd.

"PDT," Crabbe repeated. "Public display of temper."

⑥ Madam Spry explains

Now that the truth had been uncovered, Madam Spry was feeling very wise. Back at the city police building, she said to Inspector Crabbe, "There definitely were clues. I took photos of Miss Raintree's make-up trailer. It's quite shabby and she is working on a low-budget film. Miss Sweet, on the other hand, owns a marble mansion and has the lead in a big production."

The inspector twiddled his moustache. "I don't follow your thinking."

"It's obvious," she said. "Sonya Sweet is the more successful actress. When she talked about the diamond, she was putting on a very good act. Don't you see?"

"I—I think so."

"Besides, she clearly likes money. The diamond was a great investment. By collecting the insurance and then later selling the diamond, they planned to make a fortune."

Inspector Crabbe sighed. "Violet, you are a brilliant, truly super spy."

His praise so lifted her spirits that as she walked home with Hugo she sang at the top of her voice.

Madam Spry, the brilliant spy,
solved a case in the blink of an eye.
If you need her, don't be shy.
Just phone the watch of Madam Spry.

As she sang, traffic stopped dead and pigeons bounced on the pavement. She took no notice. She was so pleased she bought a chocolate cake for her supper and an extra big bone for Hugo.

They were almost home when they saw the bus driver who knew Madam Spry well. His bus had stopped and he was connecting it to a tow truck. Madam Spry was about to walk past when she recognised the tow rope.

"My spider wire!" she shrieked.

"It's mine," said the bus driver. "I found it hanging from the clock tower."

"I went back to the clock tower to get it! But someone had stolen it!"

"Too bad," said the bus driver. "It now belongs to me. Finder keepers."

Madam Spry's face went as red as her spy suit. "Some people are very dishonest!" she snapped.

The bus driver shrugged. "And some people are downright picky," he replied.

Madam Spry would have said more, but Hugo pulled on his lead with the strength of half a dozen sled dogs. It was time to go home and have supper.

From the author

I grew up with stories of super-heroes, men who did brave deeds, were always good and never made mistakes. To be honest, they were quite boring. As a change, I thought it would be fun to have a woman spy who was not very brave or smart, who was rather conceited, and who would have made a lot of mistakes without a clever dog to keep an eye on her. So that's how we have Madam Spry in her red leather spy suit with thirteen pockets, her fly-foot boots that walk up walls, and her patient dog Hugo.

Inspector Crabbe of the City Police needs Madam Spry's assistance. The famous blue diamond belonging to film star Sonya Sweet, has been stolen. Can Madam Spry, the very sly spy, find the culprit? Maybe she can with Hugo's help.

A word of warning—this is a shaggy dog story with a fishy ending.

Joy Cowley

From the illustrator

I had a great time illustrating the Madam Spry books. When I like the stories I illustrate, the pictures always seem to come out better and are easier to draw.

Each story is full of great images so the images for the covers and chapter headings were easy to choose. The stories are like fast-moving cartoons or adventure movies ... one minute we are down in the deep sea, then we are climbing the sides of high-rise buildings, being caught in traps, dealing with fiendish villains, making lucky escapes—and more.

Being the illustrator, I was with Madam Violet Spry, the very sly spy, every step of the way. How lucky can you get.

Have fun with Madam Spry. I did.

Gaston Vanzet